Chloe's Code Red

By: Lonise Love

Chloe's Code Red
By: Lonise Love

Printed in the United States of America.

ISBN-13: 978-0-578-32571-2

Book Cover/Illustrator: Qupid Art

Book Cover Assistance: Latoya Benson
www.boardroomchicks.com

Book Editor: Shanice L. Stewart of Red Ink Editing Services RedInkEditing2017@gmail.com

Contact Information:

Email: LoniseReneLove@gmail.com
Instagram: @LovingLoniLove_
Facebook: Lonise Rene'
YouTube: Loving Loni

Dedication

I dedicate this book to all the young girls, who have already or will be starting their monthly cycle soon. This is a special time of your life, and you should embrace the moment of entering womanhood.

Acknowledgements

First, I want to thank God, Jesus, and the Holy Spirit for giving me this vision and guiding me to write this book. God, I thank You for putting me on track to fulfill my purpose in You. I thank You for every trial, obstacle, and distraction that came up against me, because it made me want to go even harder. God, I thank You for Your grace and Your peace that helps me get through each day. I am nothing without You, and this book would not be possible if it was not for the Lord on my side. I am super grateful and excited for this next chapter in my life.

I want to thank my amazing Mommy! Thank you for giving me life and always being just a phone call away. Thank you for all the resources needed to write this book. I appreciate you for always going above and beyond for me. I am super grateful to have an amazing and selfless mother like you. I don't know where I would be without you. I love you!

Next, I want to thank my second mom, big sister and mentor, Shanice! You are truly an inspiration, and I thank you for pushing me to my fullest potential. I thank you for all your encouragement, advice, and for editing my book and helping with my process. I couldn't have asked God for a better big sister. I pray that God pours into you 100-fold for how you have poured into me. I love you!

I want to say thank you to my grandma, Bertha L. Penn. Thank you for your selfless love and care that you always show me. Thank you for being so willing to help me no matter the distance. You are my rock, and I appreciate your sweet and kind spirit that I'm able to experience throughout my life. You are truly one of a kind, Grandma. I love you!

I want to thank my little big brother, Shelton. Thank you for our brother/sister conversations that we have when I pick you up from football practice and school. I'm glad that even though we are eight years apart, we still have a close bond that is unbreakable. Thank you for all your support! I am proud of you! I love you!

I want to thank my father, Pastor Shelton Gordon. Thank you for instilling in me the importance of education, organization, and time management, in which I take it seriously. I thank you for being hard on me, because it helped mold and shape me into the go-getter that I am today. I love you!

I want to thank my Aunt Dean. Thank you for always being so transparent and authentic when giving me advice. Thank you for the unconditional support. You always say you got my back, and I know you mean it. I appreciate you and love you!

I want to thank my Aunt Elerie. Thank you for all your support and love with everything that I do! I admire the strength you have and how you carry it with class and grace. Thank you for setting a good example of what a true go-getter is, while being fierce and elegant. I love you!

I want to thank all my friends, who are in my corner (DMV, Atlanta, and Memphis). I love and appreciate every friend that encourages and motivates me to be the best I can be. I appreciate all the support and love that you all show me.

Table of Contents:

Introduction

Life is constantly changing, and even our bodies. When I was younger, my mom gave me a book and an emergency pouch with a pair of panties, some pads, and some wipes in it. She explained to me that in life we go through many changes in our bodies, especially being a woman. She also explained to me that soon I will experience my "Code Red". I thought to myself, what is a "Code Red"?

I carried my emergency pouch with me every day in my bookbag. I always wondered when the day would come. After many months, I decided to take my emergency pouch out of my bookbag because I had so many books and school supplies. One day while I was sitting in my 6th grade math class, and I asked my teacher if I could go to the restroom. While I was using the restroom, I noticed I started my "Code Red". I was nervous and excited all in one. However, I did not bring my emergency pouch to school, so I had to take a trip to the nurse's office. The nurse gave me a pad, and even showed me how to put the pad on. When I went back to class, I felt my stomach starting to cramp up and my back started hurting too. I wasn't too frightened by this because my mom told me that this is normal. Good thing it was the end of the school day, so I was able to go home, tell my mom and take a nice shower. In this book, you will meet Chloe who is a young girl (like you), who started her "Code Red". You will learn about her experience of stepping into young ladyhood.

Chapter 1: Meet Chloe!

Hi, my name is Chloe Johnson, and I am 10 years old in the 5th grade. I attend William Stewart Fine Arts Academy, where I sing and dance at my performing arts school. I have twin little brothers named Chance and Chase, who just turned 3 years old. My mom is a Chef, and has her own restaurant called *Vegan Fresh*. My dad is a Cardiologist (a doctor who specializes on hearts) at Emory Hospital. We live in Atlanta, Georgia in a nice house with a pool and playground in the backyard. I have three best friends named Toya, London, and Sydney. We are better known as the "Fab Four". We have been best friends since we were in kindergarten. We all attend the same school, and we are all in the 5th grade.

Ever since I was 2 years old, I have loved to dance and sing. I tried tennis, playing the piano, and running track, but I learned that those activities just weren't for me. Dancing and singing comes natural to me. Our school's Annual Spring Dance Recital is coming up in a few days, and we have been practicing everyday afterschool for the past month. A few weeks ago, three girls, including myself had to audition for the solo part. Guess what? I got the solo part in the dance recital! I was so excited, but now I'm very nervous as the big day gets closer. This is my first year having a solo part in the recital and my family will be there to support me.

I was nervous to audition for the solo part, but my dad encouraged me to believe in myself. He also told me that I can do whatever I put my mind to. I remember when I was five years old, and dad was teaching me how to ride my bike. I kept falling off and I wanted to give up, but dad would not allow me to give up. He encouraged me to be patient with myself and to keep trying.

That same night, I learned how to ride my bike without dad guiding down the street. So, anytime I'm going through a difficult or challenging time, I think about this moment in my life when I didn't give up.

Chapter 2: The Big Recital

It was finally the day of the recital, and my stomach started hurting really bad. So, I went into my parents' room to tell them how I was feeling. My mom quietly walked me out of the room, so that I would not wake up dad. He was sleeping from working all night at the hospital. Mom and I walked downstairs together and went into the kitchen. Mom got me a slice of cinnamon and raisin toast and a cup of warm water with fresh lemon juice.

The twins came downstairs laughing so loud! Chase was telling one of his silly knock-knock jokes. I was starting to feel better, so I helped mom by making the twins a bowl of *Captain Crunch* cereal in their favorite superhero bowls. Chase likes Superman and Chance likes Black Panther. I was so happy that my stomach stopped hurting, I hurried upstairs to pack up everything for the dance recital and rushed out of the house to catch my school bus.

As I arrived at school, I saw some teachers and staff setting up for the Annual Spring Recital. There's a big banner outside the school that says, "William Stewart Fine Arts Academy's Annual Spring Recital", with silver and gold star balloons around it. As I entered the school doors, I saw more balloons and our principal, Mr. Weatherspoon. He asked me if I was excited about the recital. I shook my head yes and smiled nervously. He said, "Good Luck" and proceeded to talk to the next set of students who were coming through the doors. I went to the dance room to drop off my dance bag.

After I hung up my purple dance bag on the hook, I turned around and saw my three best friends smiling at me, which made me smile. They asked me if I was excited about the solo part. I explained to them how excited I was, but still very nervous. Sydney said, “Chloe, you are going to do amazing!” Toya said, “Girl, you got this! Just be confident and give it your all.” And London gave me a hug and said, “Chloe, you have been dancing for years and it comes natural for you, so don’t worry about anything.” I love how supportive my friends are, they really made me feel better about the solo part. The school day is half a day since the Spring Recital is today. I love when we have a half a day school schedule, because we don’t have to go to every class, and we get to do a lot of fun activities.

It was call time for the recital, so Mr. Weatherspoon got on the intercom to announce that everyone who is a part of the recital must head to the theatre. Devin, one of my classmates yelled out loud, “What is call time?” I answered that call time is when everyone who is a part of a performance comes together to get ready for the show, maybe practice a few more times and get dressed without rushing. Toya, London, Sydney and I dropped our classwork in the classwork bin, grabbed our bags and headed straight to the theatre. Our dance teacher, who is also the director, Ms. Jones instructed us to get dressed so that we can practice, then get focused for the recital.

The recital begins in thirty minutes and my stomach starts turning. I was starting to get a little nervous again about the solo part. So, I peeked through the stage curtains and saw my family sitting in the crowd. Instantly, I became really happy, and my nerves went away. Ms. Jones then called us all together into a big circle to pray, give words of encouragement and love before going on stage. I love that we are a big family who sticks together. The music for the first dance group starts. My solo part is 5th on the list, so I patiently wait my turn and practice my dance in my head a few times. The music starts playing, and it was finally my time to walk on stage. So, I took a deep breath, went out and danced my heart out and I gave it my all! I was feeling the music and making sure I hit every dance move. After I performed, everyone was cheering for me, and I was so happy that I gave it my all and was no longer nervous.

When the recital was over, my family found me amongst the crowds of people, with gifts in their hands. Chance was holding one purple heart shaped balloon in each of his little hands. Chase was holding two balloons that said, "Congrats!" Dad handed me a gift bag and a bouquet of my favorite flowers, lilies. Mom gave me the biggest hug and kiss, "You were amazing out there, sweetheart! I am so proud of you!" Dad said, "Yes, we are so proud of you. I knew you could do it, Chlo Bear!" With the biggest smile ever, I thanked my family for their love and support. It really meant the world to me. The recital was amazing, and I was so grateful that I was able to get the solo part before going to middle school.

Chapter 3:
The Important Talk with Mom

It was the morning after the recital, and I was getting dressed for school. I went downstairs and saw that mom made some pancakes, scrambled eggs, and turkey bacon, which was my favorite breakfast. So, I quickly sat down and began stuffing my face until mom said, “Chloe, please slow down, the food is not going anywhere!” I laughed because mom says that to dad sometimes. Mom walked over to sit at the table with me. She shared with me how proud she is of me and how I am growing up so fast. I think all grown-ups always say that.

It was time for me to head to the bus stop, so I gave mom a kiss and hug. Before I left out of the door, mom said, “Chloe, when you get home this afternoon from school, we need to have an important conversation. Have a great day! I love you!" I smiled and said, "Thanks mom! I love you too!"

As I was walking to my bus stop, I started thinking about what mom wants to talk to me about. My school bus pulled up, and I saw my best friend Toya through the window. The school bus picks her up right before me. Still in deep thought, I slowly hopped on the bus and almost forgot to say good morning to Mr. Scott, the school bus driver. Toya noticed my "Good morning, Mr. Scott" wasn't filled with excitement like normal, and asked me if everything was okay. I told her yes, but I was still thinking about what my mom wants to talk to me about after school.

I thought about it all day, "What could my mom want to talk to me about?" At lunch I told my best friends that my mom said she must talk to me about something important, when I get home this afternoon. I asked them if they had any ideas of what my mom wants to talk to me about. Toya said, “Maybe she’s going to give you the boy talk.” London said, “Or what if it’s about your parents getting a divorce?” Instantly, my eyes got watery. “I hope not! I love both of my parents and I do not want them to split up!” Sydney put her arm around me to comfort me and says, “Girl, no it can’t be that. Maybe the talk will be about a family trip she’s planning soon!” I replied, “Yeah maybe, but I just can’t wait to get home to find out what it is.” London said, “Chloe, just pray about it. God knows what’s best.” So, I did just that, I prayed and asked God to ease my mind.

School was finally over, and I hurried up to pack my bookbag so that I could head home to have this important talk with mom. I even thought about it the whole way home. The bus stopped at the end of my driveway, I got off and ran home.

Mom was already standing in the doorway. She was looking so confused as to why I was running home. I asked mom, “Can we have the important talk now, because I have been thinking about it all day, and trying to figure out what it could be about?” Mom said, “Yes, we can Chloe. It’s nothing bad by the way, so there was no need for you to be worried or thinking about it all day.” She gives me a hug and instructs me to relax by taking my bookbag and shoes off. Mom wanted me to be calm and comfortable. We sat on the couch together, face to face.

She starts, “First, I want to say how proud I am of you and how you are growing into an amazing young lady. With you growing up, there are a lot of changes that will happen, especially with your body. All women go through something each month called a menstrual period, but we will call it a Code Red. A Code Red (menstrual period) is a time each month when your vagina is cleaning itself. When this happens, blood flows out of the uterus through the vagina." I quickly interrupted mom and said, "Would I have to go to the hospital?" She said, "No, you just have to put on a pad." I asked, "What is a pad, mom?" She replied, "A pad is a sanitary tissue that is layered with material to soak up all the blood, so that it does not leak onto your panties and through your clothes. Pads come in many shapes and sizes for all women and young girls."

There were so many questions and thoughts running through my mind. I asked mom, "So, this happens to all girls? Will it hurt? When will it stop? Do I have to stay home from school when it happens? Why hasn't any of my friends mentioned this before?" Mom place her hand on my leg to calm me down. With a smile she said, "Slow down, sweetheart." I talk very fast when I'm nervous about something. Mom continued, "I'm here to help you and answer all of your questions. Yes, this happens to every young girl, but at different times. Your friends may not have said anything, because they haven't experienced it yet or their mothers haven't spoken to them about their periods yet. Your period may last from anywhere between four to seven days each month. To be honest Chloe, it won't hurt but you may experience cramps." I then asked, "Mom, what are cramps?" She explained, "Cramps is a pain in your stomach area, when the muscles in your uterus are contracting. Some girls experience more painful cramps than others. Most young girls start their period between the ages of 8 and 16." I asked mom, "So, when do you think I will start my Code Red?" Mom answered, "No one can predict when they will come on their period, however, our body gives us signals when we are about to come on." I then asked Mom, "What are the signals?" She answered, "A lot of women are different, but your breast may feel swollen or tender, you may experience cramps in your stomach or pain in your back before and during your period. Your skin may start to break out and you may even have cravings for ice cream, sweets or junk food. Also, when you are on your Code Red, you may feel irritated, moody, tired, and sluggish on the days leading up to the start of your Code Red; and even during your Code Red, but that is normal. During the times you feel moody, irritated, or sad, make sure you don't take it out on your family and friends. Explain to them that you are hurting and moody, because of your Code Red and that you may need a moment to get yourself together."

Chapter 4:
London's Birthday Sleepover

After the talk with Mom, I was thinking about everything for the rest of the night, and I could not wait to get to school to tell my friends all about Code Red. I decided to write out my thoughts and feelings in my favorite purple glitter journal, that dad gave me after my recital.

As soon as I got on the school bus, Toya asked me about the talk with mom. I laughed and told her that everyone's guess was wrong and that I will tell them all together about the talk with mom. When we walked into our homeroom together, we didn't see London and Sydney yet. The school provides us with breakfast in the morning and I didn't get to eat at home. So, I ate some *Lucky Charms* and Toya ate *Cinnamon Toast Crunch*, while starting on our warm-up math worksheets. London and Sydney entered the classroom together. The whole class screamed, "Happy Birthday London!" as she walked in the room. My best friends and I rushed over to London's desk to give her a hug and her birthday gifts. Then, they asked me about the talk that I had with mom yesterday. The class was getting very rowdy, so Mrs. Mays told everyone to sit down and have a silent breakfast, while we complete our warm-up math worksheets. I didn't get to tell my friends about the talk Mom and I had, but I was going to wait until London's birthday sleepover tonight to tell them all about it.

I was so happy that it was Friday, and London's birthday sleepover was tonight. I absolutely love sleepovers, the last sleepover we all had was at Sydney's house. London said that we are going to make our own personal pizzas, desserts, play games, and have a dance competition. You know

I love to dance! So, I hurried home to pack my overnight bag and say bye to my brothers. Mom and I picked Toya up on the way to London's house for the party.

We arrived at London's house and Sydney was already there, so I kissed and hugged my mom bye as I headed to the basement where the sleepover would be. London's mom, Mrs. Williams decorated the basement so nicely with pink, white, and silver balloons. The plates, tablecloths, confetti, and ingredients to make the pizzas were all on table. There were also cute, pink cups on the table with all our names on them.

Mrs. Williams told us to wash our hands so that we could get ready to start making our personal pizzas, and that she would put them in the oven to bake. We all washed our hands, put on our cooking aprons, then started making our pizzas with our favorite toppings. There were so many choices of toppings to choose from. I love pepperonis and pineapples on my pizza, so those were the only two toppings I chose for my pizza.

As we are making our pizzas, Sydney says, "Come on Chloe, you never got a chance to tell us about the talk that you and your mom had." I replied, "Yeah, I was trying to tell you all in homeroom, but Mrs. Mays told us to be quiet. So, my mom wanted to talk to me about how I am growing up and that as I get older, my body will begin to change and how I will soon experience something called a period, but we decided to call it Code Red." Toya then says, "Oh yes, my older sister told me about that because she started two years ago and I saw some pads in our bathroom. And y'all know I'm nosey, so I asked her about it." We all start laughing because we all know how nosey Toya is!

London stops making her pizza and ask, "What's a period? Well, Code Red?" I replied, "Code Red is a time each month when a woman's uterus sheds and her vagina cleans itself. When this happens, blood flows out of the uterus through the vagina, and then we have to wear a pad in our panties to make sure that the blood does not get into our panties and leak through our clothes." Sydney replies, "Yes, my mom talked to me about it already, but why do you call it a Code Red instead of a period?" I shared with her that, it is a code word similar to a nickname for a period, but you can call it a period if you want. Code Red is the nickname that my mom came up with, and I think it fits perfectly, because no one will know what we are talking about. London asked, "So, how do you know when you are about to get your Code Red?" I answered, "Well, my mom told me that you will never know when you are about to start, it just happens and you must be prepared. You may experience cramps in your stomach leading up to your Code Red. You may also become moody and irritated, and you might even want a lot of sweets during your Code Red."

Mrs. Williams came downstairs to collect our pizzas to put them in the oven. While she did that, we picked the songs for our dance competition. I picked "Party for Me" by Jhené Aiko. London picked the song "Party" by Beyoncè, Sydney picked "Brown Skin Girl" by Beyoncè, and Toya picked "Pretty Girl Rock" by Keri Hilson. London's older sister, Leah, will be the judge of our dance competition. She gave us 20 minutes to practice our dances, and then it was show time. London went first because it was her birthday, then Toya went, next was me and Sydney wanted to go last because she was nervous. We had so much fun dancing! Leah said we all did a great job and that we are all winners.

After the dance competition, our pizzas were finished baking in the oven. So, Mrs. Williams brought the pizzas downstairs for us to eat. The pizzas we made were so hot and delicious. After we ate, we were so full that we did not want to make the desserts yet, so we decided to play a game of *Uno*, which is my favorite game. We played about six rounds of *Uno*, I won twice, London won twice, and Toya and Sydney both won once. By this time, we were ready to make our ice cream sundaes.

Mrs. Williams brought down vanilla, chocolate, and strawberry ice cream with so many different toppings to choose from: crushed *Oreos*, cookie dough balls, peanut butter chips, rainbow sprinkles, gummy bears, *mini M & M's*, strawberries, caramel, fudge, whipped cream and cherries. As we were decorating our ice cream sundaes, Mrs. Williams came back downstairs with a big pink and silver cake with candles that said, “Happy 11th Birthday London!” So, we sang *Happy Birthday* to London, and she blew out her candles.

After we sung, her mom asked if we wanted some birthday cake, but we decided to wait and just finish making our own fun sundaes first. I made a vanilla ice cream sundae, with crushed *Oreos*, strawberries, and some whipped cream. It was so yummy!

After dessert, we decided to watch our favorite movie *The Cheetah Girls 2.* We love to watch it together because we know all the songs and dance moves. We watched that until we all ended up falling asleep in our sleeping bags on the basement floor. The next morning, we made our breakfast with Mrs. Williams. We had so much fun making our own omelets! We also had French toast and a bowl of strawberries, grapes, and pineapples.

After we ate breakfast, we watched dance competition videos on *YouTube* while we waited for our parents to come pick us up. Mrs. Williams allowed us to take some birthday cake home, since we did not have a chance to eat it last night.

Chapter 5: Code Red!

After I got home from the sleepover, I was telling Mom about all the fun we had. Then, my stomach started hurting like it did the other day, so I told Mom and she let me use her heating pad again and told me to go lie down. Before I went to my room to lie down, I decided to go to the bathroom. I pulled down my panties and to my surprise, I saw two red spots. I yelled from the bathroom, "Mom, CODE RED!" She ran up the stairs and came to the bathroom, "What's going on Chloe?" I said, "I think I started my Code Red and I need a pad!"

As my mom went to get the pad, I thought maybe that's why I was cramping the other day before the recital and this morning. Mom went to her bathroom to get some pads for me, but she came back with this red pouch and handed it to me. I said, "Thank you Mom, but what's this pouch for?" She opened it up and I saw that the pouch included two pads, a pair of panties, some wipes. Mom explained to me that this is my personal Code Red pouch, and how I should carry it with me when I'm about to start my Code Red in order to be prepared. Mom explained again that the pads are to be placed inside of your panties. However, sometimes you might have an accident and may need to change your panties, so that's why the extra pair of panties are needed in your personal Code Red pouch. Also, the wipes are used to clean yourself off when you are unable to get in the shower. Mom even explained how hygiene is super important, especially when you start your Code Red. She said that the blood sometimes has a strong smell to it, so that's why it is important to shower but if you are unable to get in the shower, then you can clean yourself with wipes.

I then got off the toilet and stepped into the shower. The warm shower water made my cramps go away and made the blood stop for a while. After I got out of the shower, I dried off completely and I got some panties and a pad out of my pouch. Mom then came into the bathroom and showed me how to put the pad in the middle of my panties, and to make sure to flap and stick the pad wings onto the sides of my panties, so that the pad does not slide or move. Mom gave me a tip to put some tissue down to layer the pad just in case my Code Red flow is heavy. I wanted to be on the safe side, so I layered my pad with tissue just like mom said.

I put on my purple robe and walked to my room. After I put on some lotion and deodorant, I put on my favorite sweatpants and t-shirt. I decided to lie down because my cramps started to come back. I felt very irritable and moody just like mom said some women feel when they come on their Code Red. I honestly couldn't wait to get to school to tell them my best friends, because we were just talking about getting our Code Red at London's sleepover. I decided to lie down in my bed to rest my body, but I ended up falling asleep. Mom came into my room to check on me and asked how I was feeling. I told her that I was feeling a little better. Mom said, "I'm so glad you are feeling better, sweetheart. Get dressed, we are going to go somewhere." I asked, "Ok, is it just you and I going?" She answered, "Yes, just you and I are going. Dad and the boys are going to the park."

I was super excited to go somewhere with mom, but I couldn't think of where she could be taking me. Mom came into the room with a nice sundress on and some sandals, so I put on a dress and some sandals as well. We kissed and said goodbye to dad and the boys, and we left the house. As we were driving, I was constantly looking out of the window to see if I saw anything that looked familiar. I was trying to at least get an idea of where we could be going. We pulled up to Mom's favorite nail salon and parked.

Before we got out of the car, Mom explained that when you come on your Code Red, it is important to treat yourself to something nice. Mom said, “Today, we will celebrate you stepping into full ladyhood and we are going to get our nails and toes done.” I got really excited, because this was my first time coming to the nail salon. I normally polish my own nails for fun at home.

I jumped out of the car and held mom’s hand to cross the street. As we were crossing the street, I was thinking about what color I was going to pick. We entered the nail salon and the receptionist at the desk asked us what service we would like. Mom replied, “Two mani-pedis please." I whispered to Mom, "What are mani-pedis?" She answered, "Manicures means getting your nails done and pedicures means getting your toes done." They told us to pick out our color from the wall full of nail polish. They had every color in the rainbow and more, which made it hard for me to choose. After looking at all the colors, I picked my favorite color, purple. Mom picked white because that was her favorite color to get for her nails. The nail technician instructed us to sit in the big chairs with the foot tubs connected. Mom and I sat next to each other and one of the nail technicians ran the water and put soap in the bowl for our feet to soak. The big chairs also gave us back massages and we felt so relaxed. Mom asked me, "So Chloe, how are you feeling?" I replied, "I am feeling much better and very relaxed." The nail technician worked on mom and me at the same time, and they polished our nails and toes so pretty.

After the nail salon, mom said that there was one more place that she wanted to take me. I was thinking about what it could be. We got in the car and I started looking around to see where we could be going next. We then pulled up to my favorite frozen yogurt place called, *Sweet Treat.* I was super excited and I already knew what I was going to order. We got out of the car and walked inside *Sweet Treat.* As we walked inside, the lady behind the counter greeted us by saying "Are you ready to have a super *Sweet Treat* day?" With a big smile, I said, "Yes".

I went up to the counter and told the lady that I wanted to order birthday cake flavored frozen yogurt, with crushed *Oreos*, strawberries, and sour gummy worms. Mom ordered her favorite too; cheesecake flavored frozen yogurt, with strawberries, graham cracker crumbs, and whipped cream. Mom suggested for us to eat our frozen yogurt outside on the patio, since the weather was so nice today. While we were eating our frozen yogurt, mom asked me how I was feeling again. I told her that I was feeling much better. Mom said, “Good, because when your Code Red comes, it is important to treat yourself like the princess you are, by doing nice and relaxing things for yourself”. Then, mom asked if I had any more questions about coming on my Code Red, and I answered “Yes, I do!” I asked mom, if I would still be able to dance when I am on my Code Red. Mom said, “Sure. Just because you are on your Code Red, does not mean that you can’t dance or still do fun things. Those are actually the times where you need to have fun and treat yourself nicely; since you may have cramps or feel irritated and moody during that time.” I asked Mom again, “How long does it last?” She replied, “Usually up to a week, but every woman’s body is different.”

I thought about how I was only on my first day of my Code Red, but it already felt like a week. Mom finished her frozen yogurt, but I decided to take the rest of my yogurt home. As we stood up from the table, I notice that I have not changed my pad in a long time, and it feels like it is kind of leaking. Mom said, "You have your Code Red pouch with you right?" I replied, "Yes". Then I went to the bathroom to change my pad before we headed back home. I came back from the bathroom and was happy that I was prepared with my emergency Code Red pouch. I said to mom, "Thank you for giving me this emergency Code Red pouch and talking to me about stepping into ladyhood, because it was right on time." Mom replied, "No problem, Chloe. I love you and I'm here for you always." We headed back home to have movie night with dad and the boys.

Chapter 6: So, It Begins

It was Monday morning, which was day three of me being on my Code Red. I was not cramping as much as I was the first two days, so I was happy about that. I was really excited to get to school to share with my best friends what happened to me this weekend.

When I got to homeroom, I sat down and ate my breakfast while waiting on London, Sydney, and Toya to get there. Our teacher, Mrs. Mays instructed us that we could have one hour of free time on the computers when we are not in our small math groups. Sydney and London walked through the door together, they came to hug me and then went to their desk. I whispered, "Where is Toya?" and then she came running through the door telling us that she missed the school bus. Mrs. Mays said, "Ms. Toya, no ma'am, we do not run in the hallway or the classroom, sweetheart." Toya replied, "I apologize Mrs. Mays, I just did not want to be late." Mrs. Mays said, "Please make sure all homework is in the homework bin. Make sure all trash from breakfast is thrown away. Everyone should be working on their warm-up now." I knew that I had to wait to tell my friends about my weekend, because our teacher does not allow us to talk when we are completing our warm-up.

After we completed our warm-up, London went around to collect everyone's paper. Mrs. Mays called Group B over to get a table, while Group A went to the computers and Group C completes seat work until we rotate. We are all in Group A, so we headed over to the computers for free time. While we were walking over, I told them that I had to share something really important with them. We all sat down and Toya asked, "What is it, Chloe? Are you okay?" I replied, "Yes I am fine, but I started my Code Red over the weekend." London said, "Wow Chloe, we were just talking about that at my sleepover." I said, "Right, I came on when I got home from your sleepover." Sydney asked, "So Chloe, how do you feel? Does it hurt? Did you cry?" I said, "Well, I was cramping on Saturday before I even saw that I had started my Code Red. Then, I told my mom, and she gave me this Code Red pouch for me to carry. It has wipes, pads, and an extra pair of panties inside just in case I have an accident and need to change. She even showed me how to properly put on a pad. After that, I took a nap because I was cramping really bad. After I woke up from my nap, mom told me to get dressed and she took me to get my nails and toes done, and then we got frozen yogurt. I was able to ask my mom more questions about coming on my Code Red. She even explained how important it is to pamper yourself and do fun things when you come on your Code Red, because it helps you feel better."

London said, "Aww that's so nice, Chloe. But what does pamper mean?" I answered, "Pamper means to do something nice for yourself that makes you feel good. After the pamper date with mom, I felt much better, especially about starting my Code Red. Mom also explained that I am stepping into full ladyhood and that it's only the beginning. I now understand that my body will continue to change, and I will continue to grow into an amazing young lady." Toya said, "Chloe, I am so happy for you, and I love your nails! I am a little excited to start my Code Red now. Do you think your mom could make me a Code Red pouch like yours once I come on?" I replied with a smile, "Yes. I am sure she will, but I will ask her for you." After our next group rotation, the bell rang for our school fire drill, so we quietly walked outside with Mrs. Mays and our classmates.

A Note from the Author:

Hey ladies! I hope you enjoyed this book about Chloe and her journey to starting her Code Red. I hope you understand that when stepping into young ladyhood, you will experience many changes in your body. It is important to make sure that you are aware of the changes to come and know that hygiene is very important. Also, when you experience your Code Red, make sure to pamper yourself and treat yourself with care.

I wrote this book to inform and prepare you for your Code Red, because not many young girls know about experiencing a Code Red and do not know what to do. I hope this book helped you to fully understand the ups and downs, and the do's and don'ts when starting your Code Red. Also, many young girls are experiencing their Code Red at an earlier age. Remember, you won't really know when your time will come, so it is important to always be prepared. I hope you enjoy your Code Red Pouch with pads and wipes in it. Be sure to put an extra pair of panties in there as well, for emergencies. Even as an adult, I still carry around my Code Red pouch just in case of an emergency. I really appreciate my mom for talking to me about my Code Red and giving me the book and pouch.

In the back of this book, you will find 12 calendar charts to keep track of your Code Red, along with stickers to mark the day when you come on and get off. Also, there is a journal section in the back of the book, if you would like to journal your experiences, thoughts, and questions. This book is yours and you do not have to share it with anyone, but your parents if they ask.

The Code Red Glossary

Code Red: Another name for menstrual cycle / period. A time each month that the uterus of a woman sheds and blood flows from the inside of the uterus to the outside of the body.

Cramps: Pain or discomfort in the stomach area that comes before or during your menstrual cycle. This happens when the muscles in your uterus contract.

Pamper: To cater to yourself by doing something fun, relaxing or nice for yourself. (Examples: Getting your nails and toes done, getting ice cream, listening to your favorite music, or getting your favorite meal.)

Flow: A word used to describe if you have a lot of blood or even a little bit of blood.

Uterus: An organ in a woman's body where a baby is stored and protected until the woman gives birth.

Cravings: A desire for a certain food, snack, or drink that you like and want it right away, due to you being on your Code Red.

Premenstrual Syndrome (PMS): A set of feelings (moodiness, tiredness, irritation) or physical changes (breast tenderness, weight gain, bloated stomach) that happens one week or a couple days before the period comes.

Hygiene: A condition or state a of cleanliness and odorless in order to make sure that you smell good. (Ex. brushing your teeth, taking a shower or bath, washing your hands, and cleaning the dirt under your nails)

Instructions on how to put on a pad:

Take the pad out of the plastic wrap. Some pads have wings to stick onto the sides of your panties. If they do, take the plastic off the sticky part, and put the pad into your panties. Be sure to tuck the wings on the sides of your panties, to make sure that it does not move. If your flow is heavy, I would suggest putting some tissue on top of the pad.

Instructions for Calendar:

You can use these calendar charts to track your Code Red for each month, by marking the day your Code Red starts and when it ends. You can also track if your flow is heavy or lite.

It is important to keep track of your Code Red, because you may experience it around the same days each month. This will help you to be prepared for your Code Red each month.

5 Signs That Your Code Red is Coming:

1. Face Breaking Out/Acne
2. Mood Swings
3. Cramping
4. Breast Tenderness
5. Feeling Bloated (stomach looking and feeling full)

Sun	Mon	Tue	Wed	Thu	Fri	Sat

What is one thing that I did special for myself during my Code Red?

____

____

Sun	Mon	Tue	Wed	Thu	Fri	Sat

What is one thing that I did special for myself during my Code Red?

____

____

Sun	Mon	Tue	Wed	Thu	Fri	Sat

What is one thing that I did special for myself during my Code Red?

____

____

Sun	Mon	Tue	Wed	Thu	Fri	Sat

What is one thing that I did special for myself during my Code Red?

____

____

Sun	Mon	Tue	Wed	Thu	Fri	Sat

What is one thing that I did special for myself during my Code Red?

____

____

Sun	Mon	Tue	Wed	Thu	Fri	Sat

What is one thing that I did special for myself during my Code Red?

____

____

Sun	Mon	Tue	Wed	Thu	Fri	Sat

What is one thing that I did special for myself during my Code Red?

____

____

Sun	Mon	Tue	Wed	Thu	Fri	Sat

What is one thing that I did special for myself during my Code Red?

____

____

Sun	Mon	Tue	Wed	Thu	Fri	Sat

What is one thing that I did special for myself during my Code Red?

____

____

Sun	Mon	Tue	Wed	Thu	Fri	Sat

What is one thing that I did special for myself during my Code Red?

____

____

Sun	Mon	Tue	Wed	Thu	Fri	Sat

What is one thing that I did special for myself during my Code Red?

____

____

Sun	Mon	Tue	Wed	Thu	Fri	Sat

What is one thing that I did special for myself during my Code Red?

____

____

Surprise!!

Chloe's Going to Middle School

will be coming out soon!! Be on the lookout for the next book!!

Made in the USA
Middletown, DE
21 March 2022